Old
SNUFFLEGRUNT'S
Prickly Night Out

by

Nick Balmforth

Illustrations by

Dorothea Buxton-Hyde

Hedgehog enthusiast **Nick Balmforth** has spent a life-time working with and for children, first as a schoolteacher and then in the children's playground industry. A writer of poetry and a technical author he pioneered and led the process of British and European safety standards in the children's indoor play industry for which he was awarded an MBE in 2012.
He maintains a hedgehog-friendly garden in Stafford with numerous prickly friends regularly visiting for night-time food, daytime sleeping and winter hibernation.

Dorothea Buxton-Hyde began painting at the age of four. After an early career painting on porcelain for the well-known pottery company Spode, she became a professional artist exhibiting widely in Wales and later in London. She has achieved the distinction of being presented to Royalty, of being elected a Member of the Fine Art Trade Guild and being listed in the "Who's Who of Professionals". Dorothea says: *"I love and enjoy painting and it's a wonderful feeling knowing that there are people enjoying my work too."*

Old Snufflegrunt
© 2018 Nick Balmforth

ISBN 978-1-5272-1615-0

Project Editor: Sally Forsyth/Chevron Publishing
Book Design: Mark Nelson
Colour illustrations: © Dorothea Buxton-Hyde

Published by Xemxija Press

Printed in Poland

CHAPTER ONE

"Snuffle-snuffle-snort-grunt-snuffle!"

STRANGE NIGHT-TIME NOISES, but coming from where? For the other creatures that shared the same garden: the squirrels in the conifers, the pond frogs, the rockery mice and the tree slumbering birds there was no need to investigate. The noises came from inside the large pile of decaying logs at the back of the tool shed. And there was equally no need for them to question who or what made the sounds. It was *Old Snufflegrunt*, the hedgehog, slowly waking up from his long deep winter sleep that is called hibernation.

For now it was spring, the air was warmer, the snow-drops were already withering and the crocuses were clustering the ground like so many candle-lights. Daffodil shoots were busily pushing through the damp earth, the bare branches of the trees and shrubs budding into new green life.

Deep inside the moss-covered log pile and part-covered by the crisp leaves and dead twigs of the previous autumn a black, button-like nose was twitching and black beady eyes were flickering awake trying hard to focus in the dusk of the evening.

And yes, throaty and nasal noises were telling all the other creatures in the garden that *Old Snufflegrunt* was awake and about to bustle his way back into action.

"Deep inside the moss-covered log pile a black, button-like nose was twitching"

CHAPTER TWO

THERE was nothing unkind in being called *Old Snufflegrunt*. He was after all a hog and his nick-name well described the pig-like noises he uttered when busily foraging for the worms, beetles, slugs, caterpillars, millipedes and earwigs that formed the largest part of his nightly diet. Sometimes his noises would become so loud they were heard by other inhabitants of the garden long before he came bustling into sight. And as for being described as "old" – well, he was now almost three years old, an age most hedgehogs don't reach, for sadly they face many life-threatening dangers.

Leaves and twigs pushed apart *Old Snufflegrunt* climbed slowly out of the haphazard pile of logs, clumsily at first for his legs had stiffened from months of being tightly curled up. He stretched, lifted his head and sniffed the night air. It had been a chilly late October when his hibernation had started and now it was early March – over four months of deep sleep, a sleep that had been interrupted only by

*"Now, when he crawled out, he had a curious,
even comical appearance"*

occasional short wanderings away from the log pile during some of the milder nights.

When he first crawled out he had a curious, even comical appearance for bedding leaves, twigs and pine needles had stuck to some of the five thousand or so of spines on his back making him look as if he was in camouflage, almost like a small, round, walking bush.

And he was hungry, very hungry. The body fat he had successfully stored up during the spring, summer and autumn had now largely been used up and had he not eaten well during those earlier months it would have been very difficult for him to survive the long harsh winter.

Although he didn't know it, *Old Snufflegrunt* had been one of the luckier hedgehogs on the housing estate. Some in search of sheltered places in which to hibernate had nested in unlit bonfires being built for Guy Fawkes Night with the obvious result. Fortunately he had found a safe place in which to sleep unharmed and undisturbed.

CHAPTER THREE

BUT first there was the need to drink for the long sleep had left his throat very dry. His sharp ears heard the welcome sound of running water; the lily pond with its little waterfall was still there at the far end of the garden. He moved in its direction but just as he got close he was forced to stop. The lower part of the garden suddenly shelved to the edge of what seemed to an animal the size of a hedgehog like a steep cliff. There had been changes in the garden over the winter months and reaching the pond below would now become very difficult for him.

Old Snufflegrunt bustled along the cliff edge eagerly looking for a way down, sniffing the ground in front of him and occasionally stopping to sniff the surrounding air. Suddenly his nostrils caught a familiar and appetising smell; a large beetle was making its way along the leaf of a plant in front of him. It was a temptation a hungry hedgehog found too strong to resist.

"But the beetle was just out of reach ..."

But it was just out of reach and in his attempts to stretch and seize his prey his front feet lost their grip and "splash" he fell headlong over the cliff and into the dark cold water of the pond beneath!

Luckily hedgehogs are good swimmers and when he had come gasping back to the surface he paddled his feet furiously finding that the pond became much shallower as he got closer to the bank. Moreover, at the water's edge large flat rocks had been placed onto which he could easily climb and pull himself out. It was as if the pond had been built with animals in mind for had it been steep-sided he would quickly have tired and certainly would have drowned. He scrambled out very glad to be on solid ground again and leaving behind only the pine needles, twigs and leaves that had been stuck to his back and that were now floating on the pond's rippled surface.

Old Snufflegrunt had swallowed a large amount of water so there was now no need for an immediate drink. After a long pause to get his breath back he looked and sniffed around, not in the hope of finding other hedgehogs for these animals much prefer their own company, but rather to remind himself of the

"Large flat rocks had been placed at the water's edge"

garden that had been his main home in previous years. He very soon discovered there had been another big change.

The long hawthorn hedge through which he had been able to walk in order to widen his hunting ground to the many neighbouring gardens, had, over the winter, been replaced by a long, solid wooden fence with not even a chink of light between the panels. That too could create difficulties for him because his nightly hunt for food included many gardens and it was not unusual for him to walk as far as two kilometres.

He was about to try to overcome this new obstacle when his ever active nose again caught appetising smells drifting down the garden in the late evening breeze. After months of not eating, following these smells became his immediate priority, but the problem now was how to reach them, for between *Old Snufflegrunt* and the direction from where they were coming was a section of the same cliff down which he had earlier fallen into the pond.

Luck however was again on his side for he found a solid wooden plank leaning against the cliff and this meant he now had the whole garden in which to roam.

The smells came from a familiar place to him – beneath the well stocked bird feeder where chopped, unsalted peanuts, sunflower hearts and mealworms had accidentally dropped to the ground from careless beaks; all tasty and welcome morsels for hungry and grateful hedgehogs.

"Fortunately, there was enough food for them both"

But as he got closer he heard a familiar sound, a crunching, munching sound; the unmistakable and unwelcome sound of another hedgehog that had found the scattered food before him and was already gobbling it down its own hungry throat!

Now hedgehogs like other animals have no manners. There is no waiting for the other to finish before moving in to see what's left. It's every hog for itself and so a fight began in typical hedgehog style, each head-butting and pushing the other, accompanied by many huffing and puffing grunts. This lasted for several minutes and then stopped with no clear winner; it was as if a truce had finally been declared.

Fortunately there was enough food on the ground for them both so they quietly set about sharing the meal.

CHAPTER FOUR

ONCE *Old Snufflegrunt's* appetite was satisfied and having given one final unfriendly stare at the other hog, he turned his attention back to finding a way out of the garden.

He then remembered that down the side of the house was a narrow, gravelled path in the middle of which was a wooden gate leading to the front. The gravel being several centimetres deep he would surely be able to scoop it out with his powerful front feet and squeeze his body under the gate, for whilst it might look too narrow a gap for such a rounded animal the spines of a hedgehog can bend backwards, allowing it to pass into spaces much smaller than its apparent size. He found the path and quickly scooped away the small stones from under the gate, flattened his body and then passed under it quite effortlessly.

It was time for a walk; bustling his way down the path like some wound-up clockwork toy, raising his head every few metres to check what scents were in the surrounding air. His ears were also constantly alert for a hedgehog's hearing like its sense of smell is very sensitive and able to detect the very quietest of sounds even the moving of grubs and worms a few centimetres under the soil.

Suddenly there was a loud scratching noise close by. He knew instantly what it was – one of the neighbourhood cats on its nightly mousing prowl was climbing up and over a nearby fence clawing the timber panels. Almost certainly it would pay unwelcome attention to him, for any creature that moves is sure to rouse a cat's natural curiosity. And sure enough it did. The unmistakable shadow of the cat, sharpened by the glow of a nearby streetlight approached cautiously in his direction.

Old Snufflegrunt responded in the way all hedge-hogs do; he curled himself up into a tight ball, tucking his nose into his tail, raising the spines on his back to an upright position and lay there patiently waiting.

Not that a cat presents any danger to hedgehogs, it doesn't, but he wasn't taking any chances. With a quick sniff and a slightly sore nose, the cat moved on and so did *Old Snufflegrunt*.

CHAPTER FIVE

THAT particular evening there was little need to break up the soil with his foraging. During the day it had rained and the ground was still very damp and soft.

Numerous worms and beetles were on the move and *Old Snufflegrunt* stopped frequently and eagerly to devour these tasty morsels. In seeking out his prey his eyesight was the least helpful of his senses, for whilst his eyes were good at seeing in the dark and able to identify major landmarks such as trees and buildings, a hedgehog's eyes are weak and see very little detail other than what is directly under its nose.

He bustled his way across lawns and patios, around trees and shrubs, down pathways and between spring flowers. Some gardens had almost nothing to offer. The few slugs and caterpillars he sniffed out were for the most part dead, their final resting places marked by small pellets scattered like tiny sugary

" ... their final resting places marked by small pellets scattered like tiny sugary cake decorations ..."

cake decorations around the plants and on the surrounding earth.

That signalled danger! Hedgehogs have memories and *Old Snufflegrunt* remembered eating one such dead slug some years back and suffering very painful stomach-ache as a result. Other hedgehogs had died; it was a lesson learnt and never to be forgotten.

Now and again he came to a sudden dead-end; solid walls and fences allowing no way through. Hedges unfortunately were becoming increasingly rare, but in some of the fences gaps had been left that were just large enough for *Old Snufflegrunt* to be able to crawl through. It was as if they had been especially made for that purpose.

"...but in some of the fences gaps had been left"

CHAPTER SIX

B Y now *Old Snufflegrunt* had travelled quite a distance and the loud noise of passing traffic was getting closer. Crossing roads was always a scary and dangerous experience for him.

All too often he had seen the sad flattened remains of other hedgehogs that had failed to make it across to the other side. Motor vehicles are one hazard against which the hedgehog's natural self-defence of curling up into a ball is of no use at all. There are only two kinds of hedgehogs on roads – the lucky ones and the dead ones. Fortunately up to now at least *Old Snufflegrunt* had been one of the lucky ones.

He reached the verge, pausing only to eat an unsuspecting juicy worm he found inching its way slowly across the damp grass. Although he didn't know it, that could very easily have been his last meal, for the blinding glare of fast

"Amazingly, the vehicle passed completely over him ..."

passing headlights and the deafening roar of approaching motor engines could be seen and heard coming from both directions. The ground he was standing on trembled under their weight and power.

But cross the road he felt he must. So the worm having been chewed and swallowed he took his chance and cautiously set foot onto the tarmac.

For one terrifying moment it seemed that was just the wrong time to cross: the large shadow of a heavy truck was fast approaching. Amazingly the vehicle passed completely over him, its giant wheels missing him by a narrow squeak. Luck again had been on *Old Snufflegrunt's* side but this time it had been a very narrow escape!

Now safely across the road more gardens were within his reach to explore, more food to hunt out. A low level shallow water feature gave him a welcome refreshing drink and he gratefully gobbled up an unexpected bowl of meaty cat food found on a patio.

CHAPTER SEVEN

VERY close to the housing estate was an area of open space with a few hills, smaller mounds, clusters of trees and low-lying wild shrubs. Tempting though it looked to a wild animal, *Old Snufflegrunt* had never really explored it, preferring instead the daytime shelter opportunities and the natural food that most neighbourhood gardens provided. However this evening he decided to sniff it out and to see what it offered. It could have been and almost was a fatal decision!

He had only been walking a few metres over the rough ground when a snorting, panting sound was heard in front of him; moreover it was getting closer. At first he thought it might be another hedgehog but the noises were too loud and somehow different and there was also an unfamiliar scent. *Old Snufflegrunt* stopped, his instincts telling him he was in real danger.

And he was right; through the darkness a large, rounded shape with long legs was approaching and the last thing that *Old Snufflegrunt* saw before rapidly curling himself up into as tight a ball as he could was a broad brown and white head with jaws half open and a long pink tongue hanging wet and loose between fearsome looking teeth. This beast of the night was in fact a large and powerful stray dog and it could now be a matter of life and death for some dogs have been known to attack, harm, and even to kill hedgehogs.

Tight in his ball *Old Snufflegrunt's* spines were standing high like a spiky shield of armour. The hound sniffed menacingly and then with nose and paws rolled him over several times. *Old Snufflegrunt* hissed loudly. Would his sharp spines be enough to make the animal lose interest and move off in search of easier prey? He could only hope so.

The next minutes seemed like hours. Then suddenly the fearsome nosing and pawing stopped and *Old Snufflegrunt's* ears picked up the welcome sound of his attacker moving away. There was silence, but judging it was still not safe to uncurl he lay tight and motionless, all his senses working hard to be absolutely certain the danger really had passed.

Only when he was sure that it had did he slowly and very cautiously uncurl, stretch himself out to his full length, look and sniff around and then prepare to move. He was lucky to still be alive.

CHAPTER EIGHT

BY now the sky in the east was getting lighter. It was time for *Old Snufflegrunt* to end his night's foraging and unexpected adventures and to head back to the garden that had provided him with safe shelter over the winter. This time the road was much quieter and he crossed safely, finding his way through garden after garden before finally arriving back at the gravel path. He squeezed again under the wooden gate using the same scooped out gap he had made the evening before.

Now he felt safe. He was in the part of the garden he liked best; it offered thick vegetation, a variety of insects and worms on which to feed and very importantly many hiding places, because hedgehogs are by nature shy and secretive animals.

He climbed back up the wooden ramp just as the sun was rising like a jewel in the sky and headed in the direction of the log pile at the back of the shed.

Suddenly something unexpected and unfamiliar caught his eye. It was an invitingly dark entrance to what looked like a wooden box.

He was curious and moved towards it, sniffing the smell of dry straw.

Poking his head cautiously into the box *Old Snufflegrunt* nosed around. It was dark and it was dry, and there was enough space, straw and dead leaves inside to provide a cosy place in which to sleep. Compared to the old log-pile which was not able to keep out all the winter weather this shelter was much more inviting. He walked inside.

This could almost have been made for a tired hedgehog he thought as he curled up in the bedding, made a nest and closed his eyes.

Perhaps it had been.

"Poking his head cautiously into the box,
Old Snufflegrunt nosed around."

OLD SNUFFLEGRUNT

By Nick Balmforth

Snuffling, bustling helter-skelter
Night-time wakes from winter shelter
Like some spiny clockwork toy
All senses for the night employ

Ears pricked for any insect sound
Nose twitching close to hunting ground
Worms, slugs, beetles, millipede
All things tasty for the feed

Grunting through the undergrowth
Foraging fast, no time for sloth
Startled, curls up in a ball
Danger's past, it's time to crawl

But perils threaten this favoured beast
Humans the culprits not the least
Too many gardens too neat and trim
Slug pellets, pesticides – his life makes grim

Hedges scarce, now far too few
Fences, walls with no way through
Too little supporting habitat
And crossing roads can leave him
FLAT!

SO WHAT DO YOU NOW KNOW ABOUT HEDGEHOGS?

SOME PRICKLY QUESTIONS

1. *What is a hedgehog's long sleep called?*

   Hibernation

2. *In which season of the year do hedgehogs wake up from their long sleep?*

   Summer

3. *Are you more likely to see hedgehogs in the daytime or at night?*

   Night

4. *About how many spines are on an adult hedgehog's back: 50; 500 or 5,000?*

   ....

5. *Name four creatures that a hedgehog eats:*

   Beetle, Worm, Catterpillor, Millipede

6. Can hedgehogs swim?

    Yes ....

7. Name three man-made hazards that hedgehogs face:

    Cats, Motor bike, Normal bike. ....

8. What do hedgehogs do when there is danger?

    curl in a ball. ....

9. Do hedgehogs live in groups or mostly on their own?

    ....

10. Which night of the year is particularly dangerous for hedgehogs?

    ....